Aladd

Illustrated by
Gill Guile

Brimax · Newmarket · England

An old Chinese magician is looking for a magic lamp. He knows it is in a cave. The way into the cave is down a long tunnel. The magician is afraid to go into the tunnel because anyone who touches its walls will die. The magician decides to ask a boy named Aladdin to go down the tunnel and get the lamp for him.

The magician gives Aladdin
a magic ring to wear. "It will keep
you safe," he says.
"Safe from what?" asks Aladdin,
but the magician does not tell
him. Aladdin is gone for a long
time. The magician thinks he is
dead. At last the magician sees
Aladdin coming back.
"Give me the lamp," he says.
"Help me out first," says Aladdin.

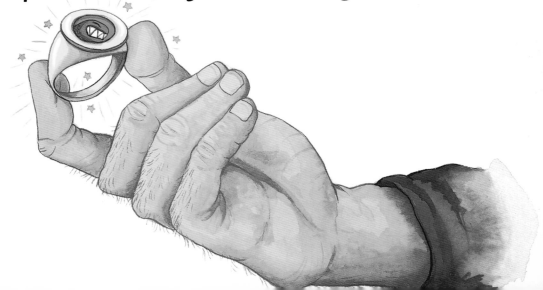

The magician is angry. "If you will not give me the lamp, you can stay there forever!" The magician says a magic spell. The entrance to the tunnel is covered with a big rock. Aladdin is trapped. By chance, he rubs the ring on his finger. Suddenly a genie appears and says, "I am the genie of the ring. Your wish is my command." "Take me home," says Aladdin.

Suddenly Aladdin is back home.
He is still holding the lamp. His
mother decides to clean the
lamp. She rubs it with a cloth.
Another genie appears.
Aladdin's mother is afraid.
Aladdin asks the genie, "Who
are you?"
The genie says, "I am the genie
of the lamp. Your wish is my
command."

Aladdin asks for money and a palace to live in. The genie makes Aladdin very rich. Aladdin even marries a princess. One day, the princess hears an old man outside calling, "New lamps for old!"

"I will change Aladdin's old lamp for a new one," says the princess. Aladdin has not told her that his lamp is magic.

The princess gives the lamp to the old man. Suddenly he throws off his coat. It is the magician. "Everything that Aladdin has will be mine," says the magician. He rubs the magic lamp, and the genie appears.

"What is your command?" asks the genie of the lamp.

"Take the princess, myself and this palace to Africa," says the magician.

When Aladdin returns home, he rubs the ring on his finger. The genie of the ring appears. "Bring back the princess and my palace," says Aladdin. "Only the genie of the lamp can do that," says the genie. The genie takes Aladdin to the princess instead.

"The magician has the lamp up his sleeve," says the princess. "Put this sleeping powder in his drink," says Aladdin.

When the magician falls asleep, Aladdin takes the lamp from his sleeve. Aladdin rubs the lamp, and the genie appears.

"Take the palace and everyone in it back to China," says Aladdin. "But leave the magician here."

The genie does as Aladdin asks.

When the magician wakes up, the princess and the palace have disappeared. He looks up his sleeve for the lamp. It is gone, too. The magician never returns to China. Aladdin and the princess live happily ever after.

Can you find five differences between these two pictures?